Disney
LEARNING

Disney
MOANA

AGES
6-7
KEY STAGE 1

Multiply and Divide!

© 2017 Disney Enterprises, Inc. All rights reserved.

Scholastic Children's Books
Euston House,
24 Eversholt Street,
London NW1 1DB, UK

A division of Scholastic Ltd
London • New York • Toronto • Sydney • Auckland
Mexico City • New Delhi • Hong Kong

Book packaging by Blooberry Design

Published in the UK by Scholastic Ltd, 2017

ISBN 978 1407 16589 9

Printed in the UK by Bell and Bain Ltd, Glasgow

2 4 6 8 10 9 7 5 3 1

Welcome to the Disney Learning Programme!

Children learn best when they are having fun!

The **Disney Learning Workbooks** are an engaging way for your child to develop key maths skills alongside fun characters from the wonderful world of Disney.

The **Disney Learning Workbooks** are carefully levelled to present new challenges to developing learners. Designed to support the National Curriculum for Maths at Key Stage 1, this title offers children the opportunity to practise skills learned at school and to consolidate their learning in a relaxed home setting with parental support. With stickers and a range of activities related to the Disney film *Moana*, children will have fun while improving their maths skills.

This book covers the multiplication and division content that children will be taught in Year 2. They learn multiplication and division facts for the 2, 5 and 10 times tables and then use these facts to solve a range of number and word problems. The National Curriculum's aims are for children to develop both deep understanding and fluency in maths. Fluency is when children are able to recall or *quickly* work out information such as times table facts. A range of visual images ensures that they understand these facts. Please note that schools sometimes vary the order in which maths content is taught, so you might find topics that your child hasn't yet covered at school.

Keep sessions fun and short. Some children may want to work independently on some of the activities while others may prefer working through the exercises with you. There are also 'Take a Break' activities for your child to enjoy between sessions.

Have fun with the Disney Learning Programme!

Developed in conjunction with Nicola Spencer, educational consultant

Let's Practise Maths

This book is full of fun activities to help you practise multiplication and division.

You will use three important signs in this book

divide

multiply

equals

Tips to Help

- Find somewhere quiet to work.

- Ask a grown-up to help you read the instructions if you are not sure what to do.

- Don't worry if you make a mistake – it is an important part of learning! Just cross it out and try again.

Words you will meet

array – an arrangement of objects in equal rows:

fact family – a group of related facts that use the same numbers:

$$12 \times 2 = 24 \qquad 24 \div 12 = 2$$
$$2 \times 12 = 24 \qquad 24 \div 2 = 12$$

equal groups – groups that have the same number of objects. Whenever you divide, you separate items into equal groups.

product – the total is also called the product in multiplication:

$$2 \times 4 = \boxed{8}$$

What is division?

Division is the opposite of multiplication.

The first number in a division sentence is the product of the smaller numbers.

12 ÷ 4 = 3

or

12 ÷ 3 = 4

Sometimes division means sharing.

Gramma Tala has 12 flowers. She shares them between 3 children.

How many flowers do they each have?

12 ÷ 3 = 4

Sometimes division means grouping.

Chief Tui has 8 fishermen. Each boat must have 4 fishermen.

How many boats do they need?

8 ÷ 4 = 2

What is multiplication?

Multiplication is when you find the total for a number of identical groups.

We use the **x** sign to multiply.

It doesn't matter in which order you multiply numbers because you will get the same total.

4 x 2 = 8

2 x 4 = 8

We can read these **multiplication number sentences** like this:

Four multiplied by two equals eight.

OR

Two times four makes eight altogether.

Equals

The equals sign shows that a calculation is balanced.

2 x 3 = 1 x 6

Let's Count in 2s, 5s and 10s

Use the number line to count in 2s.

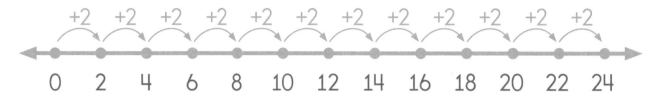

0 2 4 6 8 10 12 14 16 18 20 22 24

Moana has been collecting shells. Each shell has 2 pieces. Can you fill in the missing numbers by counting in 2s?

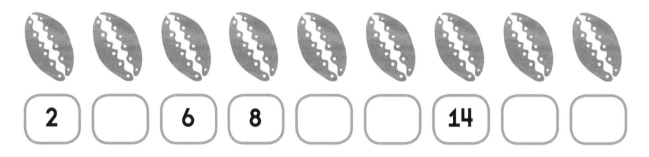

| 2 | | 6 | 8 | | | 14 | | |

Use the number line to count in 5s.

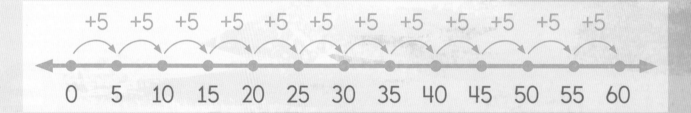

0 5 10 15 20 25 30 35 40 45 50 55 60

Some starfish have washed up on the beach. Each starfish has 5 legs. Can you fill in the missing numbers by counting in 5s?

5   15   20   30

Use the number line to count in 10s.

+10 +10 +10 +10 +10 +10 +10 +10 +10 +10

0   10   20   30   40   50   60   70   80   90   100

Tui has been collecting coconuts. Each pile has 10 coconuts. Can you fill in the missing numbers by counting in 10s?

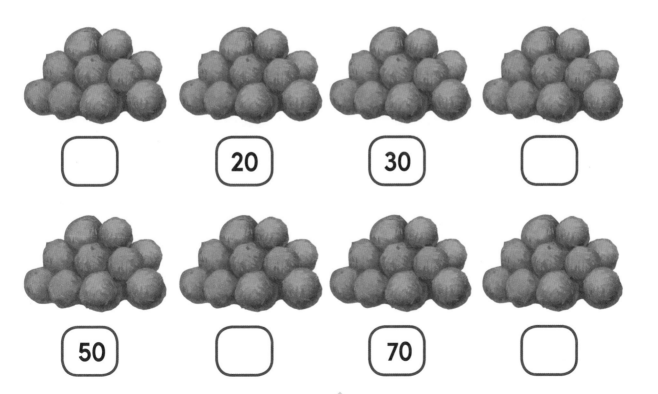

| | 20 | 30 | |
| 50 | | 70 | |

Let's learn the 2 x Table

Use the fish pictures to help you write out the 2 x table.

1	x	2	=	2
2	x	2	=	
3	x		=	
	x		=	
	x		=	
	x		=	
	x		=	
	x		=	
	x		=	
	x		=	
	x		=	
	x		=	

Complete the multiplication sentences that these pictures show:

a ( ) x (2) = ( ) flowers

b ( ) x (2) = ( ) trees

c ( ) x (2) = ( ) shells

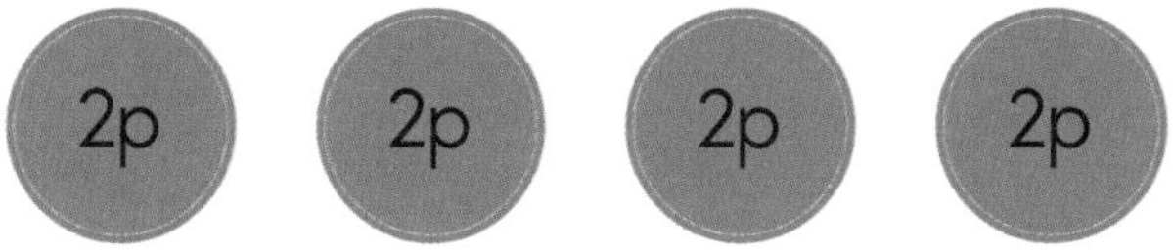

2p   2p   2p   2p

d ( ) x (2) p = ( ) p

Can you work out the missing multiplication facts in these number sentences?

e (2) x ( ) = (8)

f ( ) x (2) = (20)

g (2) x ( ) = (12)

h ( ) x (2) = (14)

i (10) = ( ) x (2)

j (24) = (2) x ( )

k (18) = ( ) x (2)

l (22) = (2) x ( )

Let's Learn the 5 x Table

Each starfish has 5 arms.
Use the arms of the starfish to help
you write out the 5 x table.

1	x	5	= 5
2	x	5	=
3	x		=
	x		=
	x		=
	x		=
	x		=
	x		=
	x		=
	x		=
	x		=
	x		=

Complete the multiplication sentences
that these pictures show:

a ( ) x (5) p = ( ) p

b ( ) x (5) = ( ) pieces

c ( ) x (5) = ( ) petals

d ( ) x (5) = ( ) dots

Can you work out the missing multiplication
facts in these number sentences?

e (5) x ( ) = (15)   **i** (40) = ( ) x (5)

f ( ) x (5) = (35)   **j** (55) = (5) x ( )

g (5) x ( ) = (25)   **k** (10) = ( ) x (5)

h ( ) x (5) = (60)   **l** (5) = (5) x ( )

11

Maui's tattoos are incredibly important to him because they represent his adventures.

Colour in the drawing of Maui's tattoos below.

When Moana was a toddler, the ocean called to her with a beautiful orange conch shell. Now it's your turn!

Follow the shell across the grid to reach the ocean.

conch shell

Start

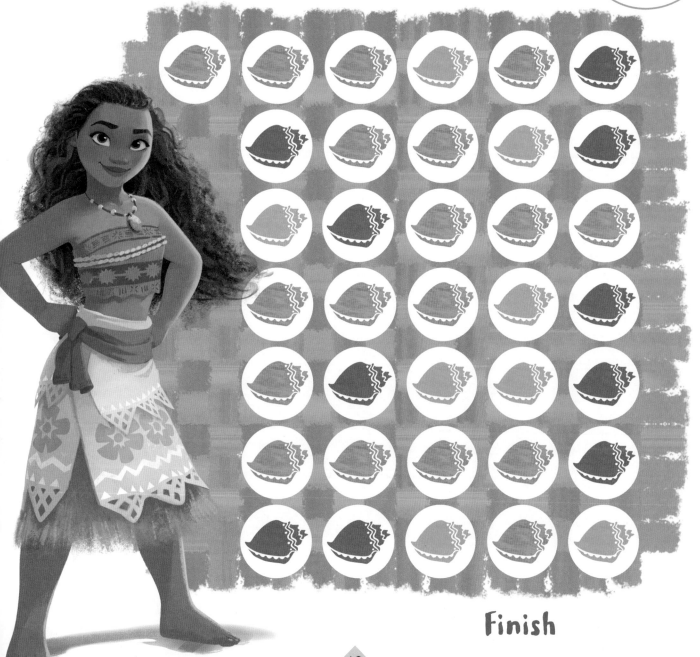

Finish

Let's Learn the 10 x Table

Each sun has 10 sunbeams around it. Use the sunbeams to help you write out the 10 x table.

1 x 10 = 10		
2 x 10 =		
3 x ☐ = ☐		
☐ x ☐ = ☐		
☐ x ☐ = ☐		
☐ x ☐ = ☐		
☐ x ☐ = ☐		
☐ x ☐ = ☐		
☐ x ☐ = ☐		
☐ x ☐ = ☐		
☐ x ☐ = ☐		
☐ x ☐ = ☐		

Complete the multiplication sentences that these pictures show:

a ( ) x (10) = ( ) leaves

b ( ) x (10) = ( ) bugs

c ( ) x (10) p = ( ) p

Can you work out the missing multiplication facts in these number sentences?

d (10) x ( ) = (30)

e ( ) x (10) = (100)

f (10) x (8) = ( )

g ( ) x (10) = (110)

h (120) = (10) x ( )

i ( ) = (10) x (5)

j (10) = ( ) x (10)

k (20) = (10) x ( )

15

Let's Learn More About Multiplication

Multiplication is a quick way to add together lots of the same number!

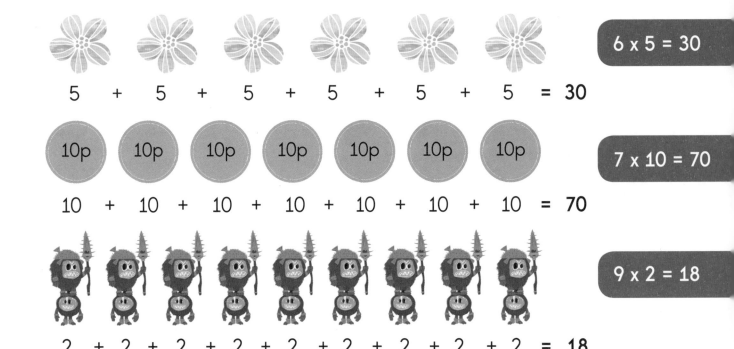

5 + 5 + 5 + 5 + 5 + 5 = **30**   6 x 5 = 30

10 + 10 + 10 + 10 + 10 + 10 + 10 = **70**   7 x 10 = 70

2 + 2 + 2 + 2 + 2 + 2 + 2 + 2 + 2 = **18**   9 x 2 = 18

Look at the addition number sentences below. Can you write out how they should look as multiplication sentences? Then work out the totals.

2 + 2 + 2 + 2 + 2 + 2 = **a** ☐ x ☐ = ☐

4 + 4 = **b** ☐ x ☐ = ☐

10 + 10 + 10 + 10 + 10 + 10 + 10 + 10 + 10 = **c** ☐ x ☐ = ☐

5 + 5 + 5 + 5 = **d** ☐ x ☐ = ☐

3 + 3 + 3 + 3 + 3 = **e** ☐ x ☐ = ☐

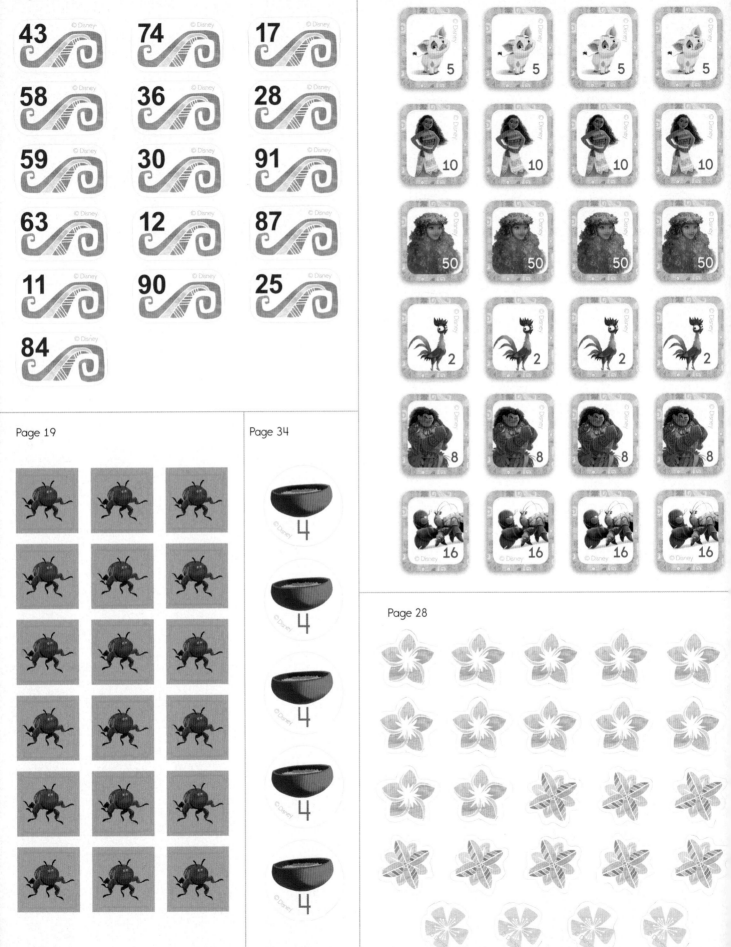

Page 18

43 74 17
58 36 28
59 30 91
63 12 87
11 90 25
84

Page 19

Page 34

4
4
4
4
4

Page 23

5 5 5 5
10 10 10 10
50 50 50 50
2 2 2 2
8 8 8 8
16 16 16 16

Page 28

Page 35

Disney MOANA

Page 37

Moana
Maui
Tamatoa
Gramma Tala

Pages 40–41

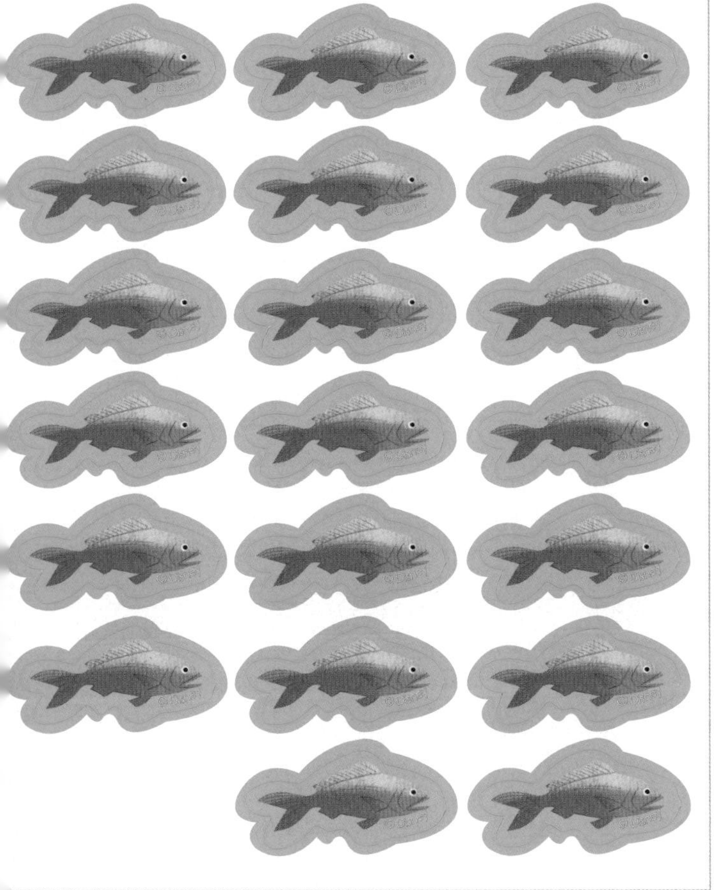

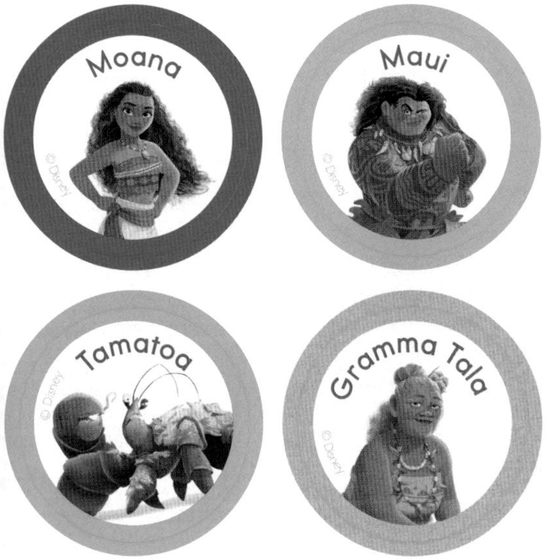

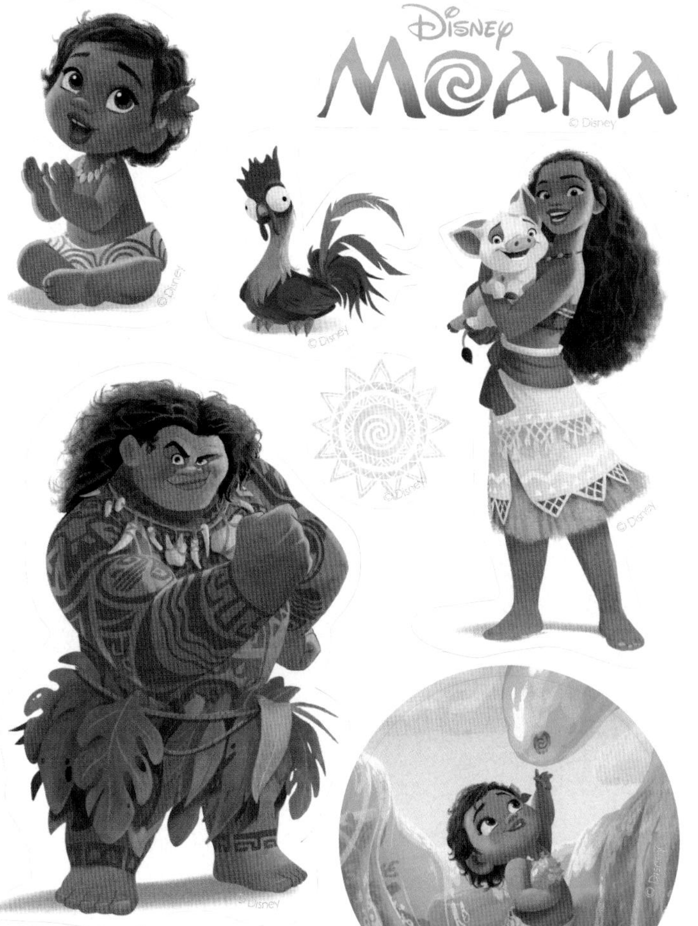

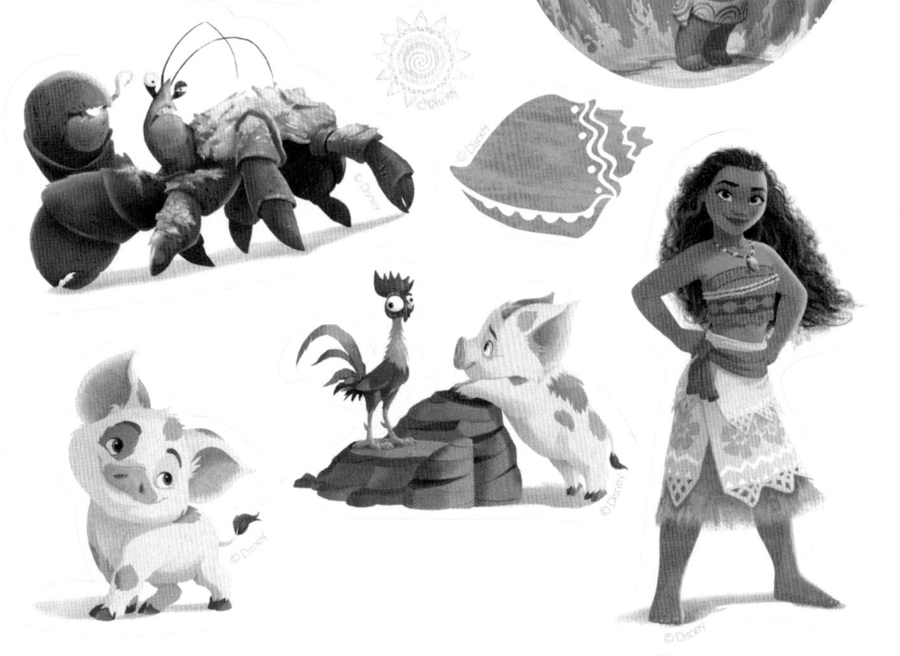

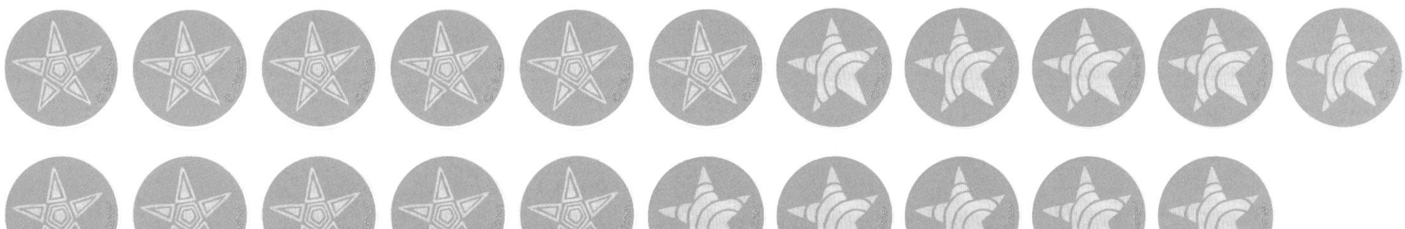

See how many objects there are in each group, then count the number of groups. Multiply the numbers together to work out the total.

Each tree has 10 coconuts.

a ◯ groups of ◯ equals ◯ .

The villager is carrying 5 fish on each side of his stick.

b ◯ groups of ◯ equals ◯ .

Each sea shell has 3 spots on it.

c ◯ groups of ◯ equals ◯ .

Circle the fish to group them correctly. The first one has been done for you.

3 twos

d 4 fives

e 10 threes

Let's Play with 2s, 5s and 10s

Odd numbers always end in 1, 3, 5, 7 or 9 and even numbers always end in 0, 2, 4, 6 or 8.

Colour even numbers in orange and colour odd numbers in blue.

What pattern do you notice?

1	2	3	4	5	6	7	8	9	10
11	12	13	14	15	16	17	18	19	20
21	22	23	24	25	26	27	28	29	30
31	32	33	34	35	36	37	38	39	40
41	42	43	44	45	46	47	48	49	50
51	52	53	54	55	56	57	58	59	60

Multiples of 2 are all even numbers. Even numbers can be divided into groups of 2 without any left over.

Find the numbered wave stickers on the sticker sheet. Look closely at the numbers and put them into the correct box below.

Odd Numbers	Even Numbers

18

An array is an arrangement of objects in equal rows.

Arrays are a useful way of showing how multiplication and division are connected.

This array represents (5) x (3) = (15). It also shows other facts. We call the group a 'fact family'.

3 x 5 = 15

15 ÷ 3 = 5

15 ÷ 5 = 3

Complete the fact family for these flowers

a ◯ x ◯ = ◯

◯ x ◯ = ◯

◯ ÷ ◯ = ◯

◯ ÷ ◯ = ◯

Use some bug stickers to make a 6 x 3 array and complete the fact family.

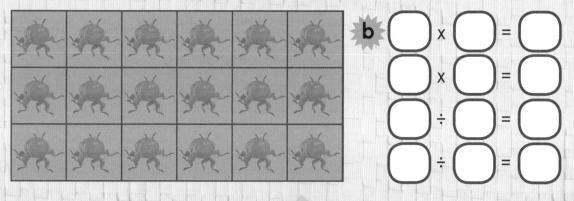

b ◯ x ◯ = ◯

◯ x ◯ = ◯

◯ ÷ ◯ = ◯

◯ ÷ ◯ = ◯

Colour in this picture of Moana
helping a baby turtle.

Can you find the words below
in the word search?

times   fact   add

multiple   share   total   groups

divide   product   multiply   equals

```
M T E M E Q U A L S O
U G M K U S S Z W F I
L R M B E O T O T A L
T O U L P R O D U C T
I U L Y V A Q U D T E
P P T I M E S M F O K
L S I W C H S S I R P
E B P A D D H Q O I P
A G L J U H A S N M R
C M Y L U O R E A U O
A D I V I D E L M L D
```

Let's Multiply in Any Order

You can multiply two numbers in any order. You will get the same total. Another way of saying this is that multiplication is 'commutative'.

Can you fill in all of the gaps below?

5p 5p

a ☐ groups of five pence equals ☐ pence.
☐ p x ☐ = ☐ p

2p 2p
2p 2p 2p

b ☐ groups of two pence equals ☐ pence.
☐ x ☐ p = ☐ p

Work out how many of each coin you would need to make the product of each calculation.

c 2p x ☐ = 20p
☐ x 2p = 20p
5p x ☐ = 20p
☐ x 5p = 20p

d 30p = 10p x ☐
30p = ☐ x 10p
30p = 2p x ☐
30p = ☐ x 2p

Write the matching multiplication fact to each number sentence below. For example, 7 x 3 = 21 and 3 x 7 = 21.

e 3 x 8 = 24

f 9 x 2 = 18

g 3 x 4 = 12

_____   _____   _____

Unlike multiplication, division is not commutative. You have to start your number sentence with the total.

a Here are some 5, 10 and 50 number cards. Find the matching stickers to fill in these number sentences.

[ ] x [ ] = [ ]   [ ] ÷ [ ] = [ ]

[ ] x [ ] = [ ]   [ ] ÷ [ ] = [ ]

b Now use the 2, 8 and 16 number card stickers to fill in these number sentences.

[ ] x [ ] = [ ]   [ ] ÷ [ ] = [ ]

[ ] x [ ] = [ ]   [ ] ÷ [ ] = [ ]

Can you circle the incorrect number sentences below?

c

3 x 10 = 30   3 ÷ 30 = 10

10 x 3 = 30   30 ÷ 10 = 3

d

9 x 2 = 18   18 ÷ 2 = 9

2 x 9 = 18   2 ÷ 9 = 18

23

Let's Solve Multiplication Problems

Read each problem. Can you write a number sentence and then use multiplication facts to work out the answer?

a As a bug, Maui has 6 legs. How many legs would 2 bugs have?

6 x ◯ = ◯   ◯ legs

b Maui can turn into a hawk. Hawks have 8 talons. How many talons would 3 hawks have?

◯ x ◯ = ◯   ◯ talons

c Maui has 9 teeth on his necklace. How many teeth would 2 necklaces have?

◯ x ◯ = ◯   ◯ teeth

d In the village there are 12 palm trees.
There are 5 coconuts on each tree.
How many coconuts are there altogether?

◯ x ◯ = ◯   ◯ coconuts

e Sea turtles have 4 flippers. How many
flippers do 10 turtles have altogether?

◯ x ◯ = ◯   ◯ flippers

f One shell is 5 centimetres
long. How long is a row
of 6 shells?

5cm   5cm   5cm   5cm   5cm   5cm

◯ x ◯ = ◯   ◯ cm long

g Moana has collected 4 piles of 10 coconuts. Tui
has 3 baskets of 5 coconuts. Who has the most?

◯ x ◯ = ◯

Moana has ◯ coconuts

◯ x ◯ = ◯

Tui has ◯ coconuts

_____ has more coconuts than _____ .

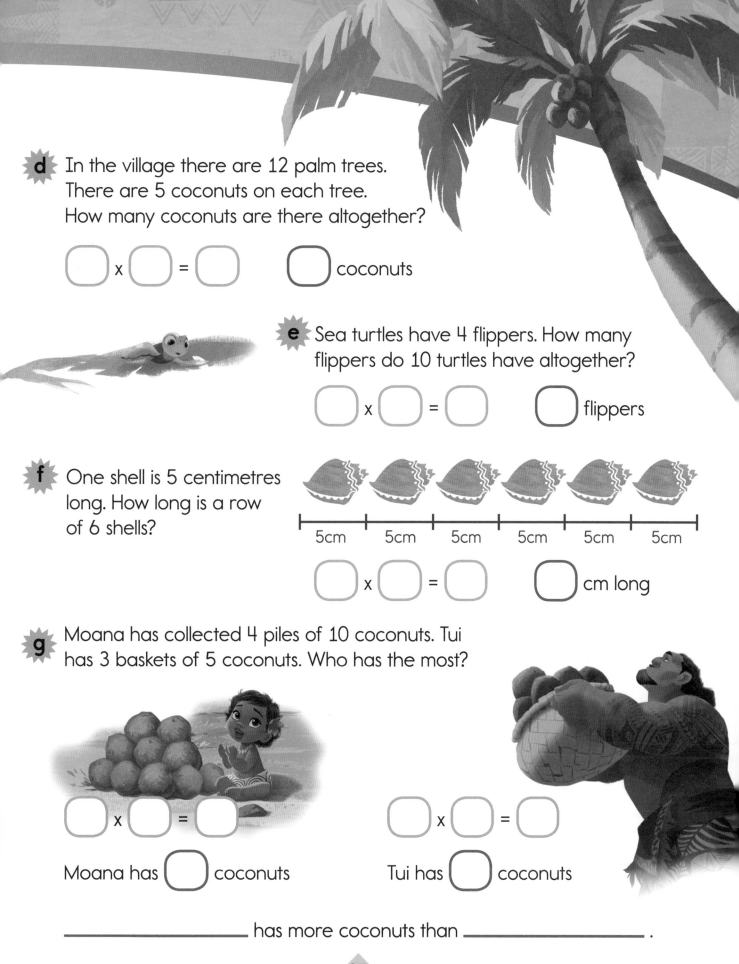

25

Let's Double and Halve Numbers

Doubling is the same as multiplying by 2.

double 3 is 6

3 x 2 = 6

a Double 4 is ⬜   **b** Double 10 is ⬜   **c** Double 3 is ⬜

d Double 12 is ⬜   **e** Double 7 is ⬜   **f** Double 9 is ⬜

Halving is the same as dividing by 2.

half of 10 is 5

½ of 10 is 5

10 ÷ 2 = 5

g Half of 14 is ⬜   **h** Half of 20 is ⬜   **i** Half of 16 is ⬜

j Half of 12 is ⬜   **k** Half of 6 is ⬜   **l** Half of 18 is ⬜

When we find one quarter of a group we divide by 4. We can write one quarter like this: ¼.

One way of finding one quarter is by halving and then halving again.

One half of 8 is 4.　　One quarter of 8 is 2.

Find ½ and ¼ of these groups by colouring ½ of each group blue and ¼ orange.

a One half of 12 is ( )　　One quarter of 12 is ( )

b One half of 20 is ( )　　One quarter of 20 is ( )

c One half of 16 is ( )　　One quarter of 16 is ( )

d One half of 24 is ( )　　One quarter of 24 is ( )

Let's Solve Calculations

Solve the ÷ 2 questions by halving. 10 ÷ 2 is the same as half of 10.

a Moana is making herself and Gramma Tala flower necklaces. Find the matching stickers. Then divide the stickers equally and stick them on each necklace to decorate them.

These are the flower stickers you have to choose from.

b Work out the answers to these division calculations by using multiplication facts.

To work out 60 ÷ 10 you can ask yourself, "How many groups of 10 are there in 60?" You could count the groups on your fingers if you need to.

60 ÷ 10 = ◯   15 ÷ 5 = ◯   100 ÷ 10 = ◯   25 ÷ 5 = ◯

10 ÷ 10 = ◯   35 ÷ 5 = ◯   24 ÷ 2 = ◯   14 ÷ 2 = ◯

Can you fill out the grids by multiplying the number in the blue boxes by the number in the orange boxes?

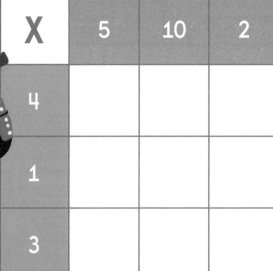

a

X	5	10	2
4			
1			
3			

b

X	6	5	10
10			
5			
2			

 c Can you fill out the missing numbers in these calculations?

40 ÷ ⬜ = 10   ⬜ ÷ 2 = 8   5 x ⬜ = 30

⬜ x 2 = 18   90 ÷ ⬜ = 10   ⬜ ÷ 10 = 6

15 ÷ ⬜ = 3   5 x ⬜ = 60   22 ÷ ⬜ = 2

⬜ x 5 = 35   70 ÷ ⬜ = 10   10 ÷ ⬜ = 5

Take a Break

Help Maui make his way from Start to Finish. Don't let him bump into any shells!

Start

Finish

The Kakamora have stolen the heart of Te Fiti!
Can you find it? Then colour the picture in!

Let's Solve Division Problems

Write a division sentence and use multiplication facts to work out the answer.

a 35 Kakamora put themselves into groups of 5 to attack Moana's boat. How many groups were there?

$\bigcirc \div \bigcirc = \bigcirc$

b Moana has 110 shells. She needs 10 shells to make one necklace. How many necklaces can she make?

$\bigcirc \div \bigcirc = \bigcirc$

c The villagers plant 45 palm trees on Motunui, set in groups of 5. How many groups are there? Draw a picture to help you solve the problem.

$\bigcirc \div \bigcirc = \bigcirc$

d Each ancient voyaging canoe has 1 sail. If they make 24 sails, how many canoes can set off on a voyage?

$\bigcirc \div \bigcirc = \bigcirc$

Read these word problems and work out the correct answers.

a Moana catches 15 fish. She shares them equally between herself and two friends. **Tick** the calculation that shows how many fish they each get.

15 – 2 = 13 ◯   15 ÷ 3 = 5 ◯

15 x 2 = 30 ◯   15 + 2 = 17 ◯   15 – 3 = 12 ◯

b Yesterday Tamatoa found 4 coins. Today he has found three times as many. **Tick** which sum shows how many coins he found today.

4 – 3 = 1 ◯   4 ÷ 3 = 12 ◯   4 + 3 = 7 ◯

4 ÷ 3 = 12 ◯   4 x 3 = 12 ◯

c 18 Kakamora sail on 3 floating islands. **Tick** the sum that shows how many Kakamora are on each floating island.

18 – 3 = 15 ◯   18 ÷ 3 = 6 ◯

8 + 10 = 18 ◯   18 – 6 = 12 ◯

3 x 5 = 15 ◯

Let's Solve Problems

Get your thinking cap on to solve these problems!

a

Moana and Gramma Tala want to buy some mangoes and share them equally. They could buy a bag of 15 mangoes, 16 mangoes or 17 mangoes.

Circle the bag that they should buy so the mangoes can be shared equally without cutting any mangoes up or having any left over. Then share the mangoes evenly between Moana and Grandma Tala.

They will each get ⬭ mangoes.

b Pua can eat his bowl of food in 4 big mouthfuls. How many mouthfuls will it take him to eat 5 bowls of food?

Find the stickers and use them to help you solve the problem.

Pua would take ⬭ mouthfuls.

c

Moana plants 6 rows of 3 pineapples. She picks two pineapples. How many are left? Draw an array or other pictures to help you.

There are ⬭ pineapples left.

d Moana, Tala and Tui went fishing and caught a total of 20 fish. Tui caught ½ of them and Moana and Tala both caught ¼ of them.

Use your stickers to show how many fish they each caught.

Use this array to help you work out ½ and ¼.

Let's Balance Calculations

Let's check whether these calculations are balanced.

The equals sign shows us that a calculation is balanced with the same total on each side.

First, write the answers to each side of the calculations in the spaces underneath. The first one has been done for you.

2 x 5 = 1 x 10

(10)   (10)

a 4 x 5 = 3 x 10

◯   ◯

b 30 ÷ 10 = 5 x 3

◯   ◯

c 50 ÷ 10 = 15 ÷ 5

◯   ◯

d 4 x 10 = 8 x 5

◯   ◯

e 2 x 5 = 20 ÷ 2

◯   ◯

Now, circle the number sentences above that are balanced.

Fill in the missing numbers to balance these equations. The first one has been done for you.

15 x 1 = [5] x 3

[15]

f 16 ÷ 2 = 80 ÷ ◯

◯

g 20 ÷ ◯ = 100 ÷ 10

◯

h ◯ x 3 = 6 x 2

◯

i ◯ x 5 = 10 x 3

◯

j 30 ÷ 3 = 5 x ◯

◯

Let's Play the Wayfinder Game

Moana and her friends must cross the ocean safely! Who will get to the other side first?

Make sure you have 2, 3 or 4 players ready to join in the fun on pages 38 and 39.

You will need:

- a piece of thin card
- scissors
- counter stickers
- a dice

How to set up the game:

1. Find the counter stickers on the sticker spread and stick them onto the card.

2. Carefully cut round the counters to create four player counters.

3. Each player chooses a game piece and places it on **START**.

4. Decide which player will go first.

Scissors are sharp! Ask a grown-up to help you.

Let's play the wayfinder game:

1. The first player rolls the dice and moves their counter the same number of spaces as the number on the dice.

2. If the player lands on a special space, they must follow the instructions, then end their turn.

3. The next player takes their turn.

4. The first player to reach **FINISH** is the winner.

Let's Play

2 — There's a storm! Miss a turn.

3

4 — Heihei appears! Jump forward 2 spaces.

16

1

5

6

15

START

7

8 — Kakamoras attack! Go back 3 spaces.

9

10

The Wayfinder Game

19 **20** **21**

18 Chased by Te Kā. **Go back 3 spaces.** **22**

The ocean helps you! **Jump forward 4 spaces.** **23**

24

17 **25**

You find food. **Jump to space 18.** **14**

28 **27** **26**

Tamatoa alert! **Go back 3 spaces.** **13**

29

12 **30**

11 **FINISH**

Here Are All the Things I Can Do

Place a star sticker next to
the things you can do!

I can use ...

- multiplication facts for the 2 x table

- multiplication facts for the 5 x table

- multiplication facts for the 10 x table

- arrays

- division facts for the 2 x table

- division facts for the 5 x table

- division facts for the 10 x table

I can understand ...

- that multiplication is repeated addition

- that multiplication is commutative

- that you cannot divide in any order (not commutative)

I can solve ...

- word problems involving multiplication

- word problems involving division

- balance problems

I can ...

- count in steps of 2, 3, 5 and 10

- write multiplication and division sentences

- describe how many equal groups are shown

- spot odd and even numbers

- double numbers to 20

- halve even numbers to 20

- find ½ and ¼ of a group

- identify the correct calculation in a word problem

Highlight maths in everyday life!

Maths is an essential skill that we use every day when we cook, shop, play and much, much more! Be positive about maths with your child, as children are quick to pick up on negative vibes that parents can give if they didn't enjoy maths at school.

Fluency with mental maths facts

One of the most important things that you can do at home, is to help your child to learn multiplication and division facts for the 2, 5 and 10 multiplication tables.

- First, they need to practise counting forwards and backwards in multiples of 2, 5 and 10. For example: 2, 4, 6, 8 … (up to 24) 5, 10, 15, 20 … (up to 60) and 10, 20, 30 … (up to 120).

- Then recite the times tables in order, starting at zero. For example: "Zero times 2 is zero; 1 times 2 is 2…" (continuing to 12 times the number).

- Next, ask your child random multiplication and division questions . What is 4 times 5? What is 8 multiplied by 10? What is 30 divided by 10?

Make the most of journeys

The journey to and from school is a great time to practise number facts. As well as times tables, you could play number 'ping pong' with doubling and halving facts. To practise doubling, you say 9 and your child pings back 18. To practise halving, you say 20 and your child pings back 10.

Tips to help

Children often find division questions harder, so encourage them to use the multiplication facts to help them work out the answer. For example, what is 30 divided by 5? If they struggle, re-word the question to ask them, how many groups of five are there in 30?

You could make colourful posters or flash cards to help your child learn their times tables. Write times table questions on one side of a flash card with the answer on the back. You could vary where the missing number is placed in the question: ___ x 5 = 20   30 ÷ ___ = 10.

Songs and chants can also help children learn times tables. Some are available online or your child could make up a song to make it more memorable.

Pattern spotting

Use a 1 to 100 number square to spot patterns for different multiplication tables. For example, multiples of 2 are always even and have either 0, 2, 4, 6 or 8 at the end. Multiples of 5 always end in a 5 or a 0. Multiples of 10 are always even numbers and end in 0. What patterns do you notice about where they are located on a number square?

The ten times table products are all double the five times table products.

Make up number stories

Fire off three numbers from a multiplication sentence and ask your child to tell you some number sentences, or make up a number story using the numbers. For example, using the numbers 4, 5 and 20 you could tell the story, "Four children all have five teddies. How many teddies do they have altogether?"

Answers

Pages 6–7

2	4	6	8	10	12	14	16	18

5	10	15	20	25	30	35	40

10	20	30	40	50	60	70	80

Page 8

2 x 2 = 4	6 x 2 = 12	10 x 2 = 20
3 x 2 = 6	7 x 2 = 14	11 x 2 = 22
4 x 2 = 8	8 x 2 = 16	12 x 2 = 24
5 x 2 = 10	9 x 2 = 18	

Page 9

a. 7 x 2 = 14
b. 3 x 2 = 6
c. 6 x 2 = 12
d. 4 x 2p = 8p
e. 2 x 4 = 8
f. 10 x 2 = 20

g. 2 x 6 = 12
h. 7 x 2 = 14
i. 10 = 5 x 2
j. 24 = 2 x 12
k. 18 = 9 x 2
l. 22 = 2 x 11

Page 10

2 x 5 = 10	6 x 5 = 30	10 x 5 = 50
3 x 5 = 15	7 x 5 = 35	11 x 5 = 55
4 x 5 = 20	8 x 5 = 40	12 x 5 = 60
5 x 5 = 25	9 x 5 = 45	

Page 11

a. 4 x 5p = 20p
b. 3 x 5 = 15
c. 7 x 5 = 35
d. 11 x 5 = 55
e. 5 x 3 = 15
f. 7 x 5 = 35

g. 5 x 5 = 25
h. 12 x 5 = 60
i. 40 = 8 x 5
j. 55 = 5 x 11
k. 10 = 2 x 5
l. 5 = 5 x 1

Page 13

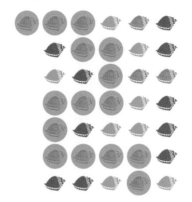

Page 14

2 x 10 = 20	6 x 10 = 60	10 x 10 = 100
3 x 10 = 30	7 x 10 = 70	11 x 10 = 110
4 x 10 = 40	8 x 10 = 80	12 x 10 = 120
5 x 10 = 50	9 x 10 = 90	

Page 15

a. 3 x 10 = 30
b. 5 x 10 = 50
c. 7 x 10p = 70p
d. 10 x 3 = 30
e. 10 x 10 = 100
f. 10 x 8 = 80

g. 11 x 10 = 110
h. 120 = 10 x 12
i. 50 = 10 x 5
j. 10 = 1 x 10
k. 20 = 10 x 2

Page 16

a. 6 x 2 = 12
b. 2 x 4 = 8
c. 9 x 10 = 90

d. 4 x 5 = 20
e. 5 x 3 = 15

Page 17

a. 3 groups of 10 = 30
b. 2 groups of 5 = 10
c. 4 groups of 3 = 12

Answers should reflect any 4 groups of 5 and 10 groups of 3.

Page 18

1	2	3	4	5	6	7	8	9	10
11	12	13	14	15	16	17	18	19	20
21	22	23	24	25	26	27	28	29	30
31	32	33	34	35	36	37	38	39	40
41	42	43	44	45	46	47	48	49	50
51	52	53	54	55	56	57	58	59	60

Odd numbers: 11, 17, 25, 43, 59, 63, 87, 91
Even numbers: 12, 28, 30, 36, 58, 74, 84, 90

Page 19

a. $4 \times 5 = 20$
$5 \times 4 = 20$
$20 \div 5 = 4$
$20 \div 4 = 5$

b. $3 \times 6 = 18$
$6 \times 3 = 18$
$18 \div 3 = 6$
$18 \div 6 = 3$

Page 21

```
M T E M E Q U A L S O
U G M K U S S Z W F I
L R M B E O T O T A L
T O U L P R O D U C T
I U L Y V A Q U D T E
P P T I M E S M F O K
L S I W C H S S I R P
E B P A D D H Q O I P
A G L J U H A S N M R
C M Y L U O R E A U O
A D I V I D E L M L D
```

Page 22

a. 2 groups of five pence = 10 pence
$5p \times 2 = 10p$

b. 5 groups of two pence = 10 pence
$5 \times 2p = 10p$

c. $2p \times 10 = 20p$
$10 \times 2p = 20p$
$5p \times 4 = 20p$
$4 \times 5p = 20p$

d. $30p = 10p \times 3$
$30p = 3 \times 10p$
$30p = 2p \times 15$
$30p = 15 \times 2p$

e. $8 \times 3 = 24$ f. $2 \times 9 = 18$ g. $4 \times 3 = 12$

Page 23

a. $5 \times 10 = 50$
$10 \times 5 = 50$
$50 \div 5 = 10$
$50 \div 10 = 5$

b. $2 \times 8 = 16$
$8 \times 2 = 16$
$16 \div 8 = 2$
$16 \div 2 = 8$

c. $3 \div 30 = 10$

d. $2 \div 9 = 18$

Pages 24–25

a. $6 \times 2 = 12$ legs
b. $8 \times 3 = 24$ talons
c. $9 \times 2 = 18$ teeth
d. $12 \times 5 = 60$ coconuts
e. $4 \times 10 = 40$ flippers
f. $5 \times 6 = 30$ cm long
g. $4 \times 10 = 40$. Moana has 40 coconuts.
$3 \times 5 = 15$. Tui has 15 coconuts.
Moana has more coconuts than Tui.

Page 26

a. 8   e. 14   i. 8
b. 20   f. 18   j. 6
c. 6   g. 7   k. 3
d. 24   h. 10   l. 9

Page 27

a. One half of 12 is 6. One quarter of 12 is 3.

b. One half of 20 is 10. One quarter of 20 is 5.

c. One half of 16 is 8. One quarter of 16 is 4.

d. One half of 24 is 12. One quarter of 24 is 6.

Answers

Page 28

a. Moana and Gramma Tala's necklaces might look like this. Your pattern might be different but they each should have the same flowers.

b. 60 ÷ 10 = 6   35 ÷ 5 = 7   25 ÷ 5 = 5
10 ÷ 10 = 1   100 ÷ 10 = 10   14 ÷ 2 = 7
15 ÷ 5 = 3   24 ÷ 2 = 12

Page 29

a.

X	5	10	2
4	20	40	8
1	5	10	2
3	15	30	6

b.

X	6	5	10
10	60	50	100
5	30	25	50
2	12	10	20

c. 40 ÷ 4 = 10   16 ÷ 2 = 8   5 x 6 = 30
9 x 2 = 18   90 ÷ 9 = 10   60 ÷ 10 = 6
15 ÷ 5 = 3   5 x 12 = 60   22 ÷ 11 = 2
7 x 5 = 35   70 ÷ 7 = 10   10 ÷ 2 = 5

Pages 30–31

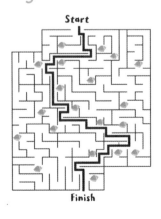

Page 32

a. 35 ÷ 5 = 7   c. 45 ÷ 5 = 9
b. 110 ÷ 10 = 11   d. 24 ÷ 1 = 24

Page 33

a. 15 ÷ 3 = 5 ✓
b. 4 x 3 = 12 ✓
c. 18 ÷ 3 = 6 ✓

Pages 34–35

a. The '16' bag. They will each get 8 mangoes.
b. Pua would take 20 mouthfuls.
c. There are 16 pineapples left.
d. Tui caught 10 fish. Moana and Tala each caught 5 fish.

Page 36

a. 4 x 5 (20) = 3 x 10 (30)
b. 30 ÷ 10 (3) = 5 x 3 (15)
c. 50 ÷ 10 (5) = 15 ÷ 5 (3)
d. (4 x 10 (40) = 8 x 5 (40))
e. (2 x 5 (10) = 20 ÷ 2 (10))

f. 16 ÷ 2 (8) = 80 ÷ 10
g. 20 ÷ 2 = 100 ÷ 10 (10)
h. 4 x 3 = 6 x 2 (12)
i. 6 x 5 = 10 x 3 (30)
j. 30 ÷ 3 (10) = 5 x 2

DISNEP
MOANA

CONGRATULATIONS

....
(Name)

has completed the Disney Learning Workbook:

Multiply and Divide!

Presented on

....
(Date)

....
(Parent's Signature)